Dedication:
To my family who both endures and encourages my weirdness. Thank you!

Paperback: 978-0-578-29212-0
First paperback edition May 2022.

Big Turd & Little Turd

Written by:

Willie Nelson

Big Turd and Little Turd are sitting in the pot.

Big Turd is stuck
but Little Turd is not.

After the flush
Little Turd is gone.

Big Turd is still floating all alone.

Big Turd and Little Turd moving apart.

Big Turd and Little Turd,
each a broken heart.

Two best friends
searching for each other.

**Feeling just like
they had lost a brother**

Big Turd and Little Turd could they ever reunite.

How could they find each other after this night.

Dad stepped in to the rescue,
with a plunger at last!

Three big plunges
and Big Turd felt a blast.

Oh! What a sight it was to behold.

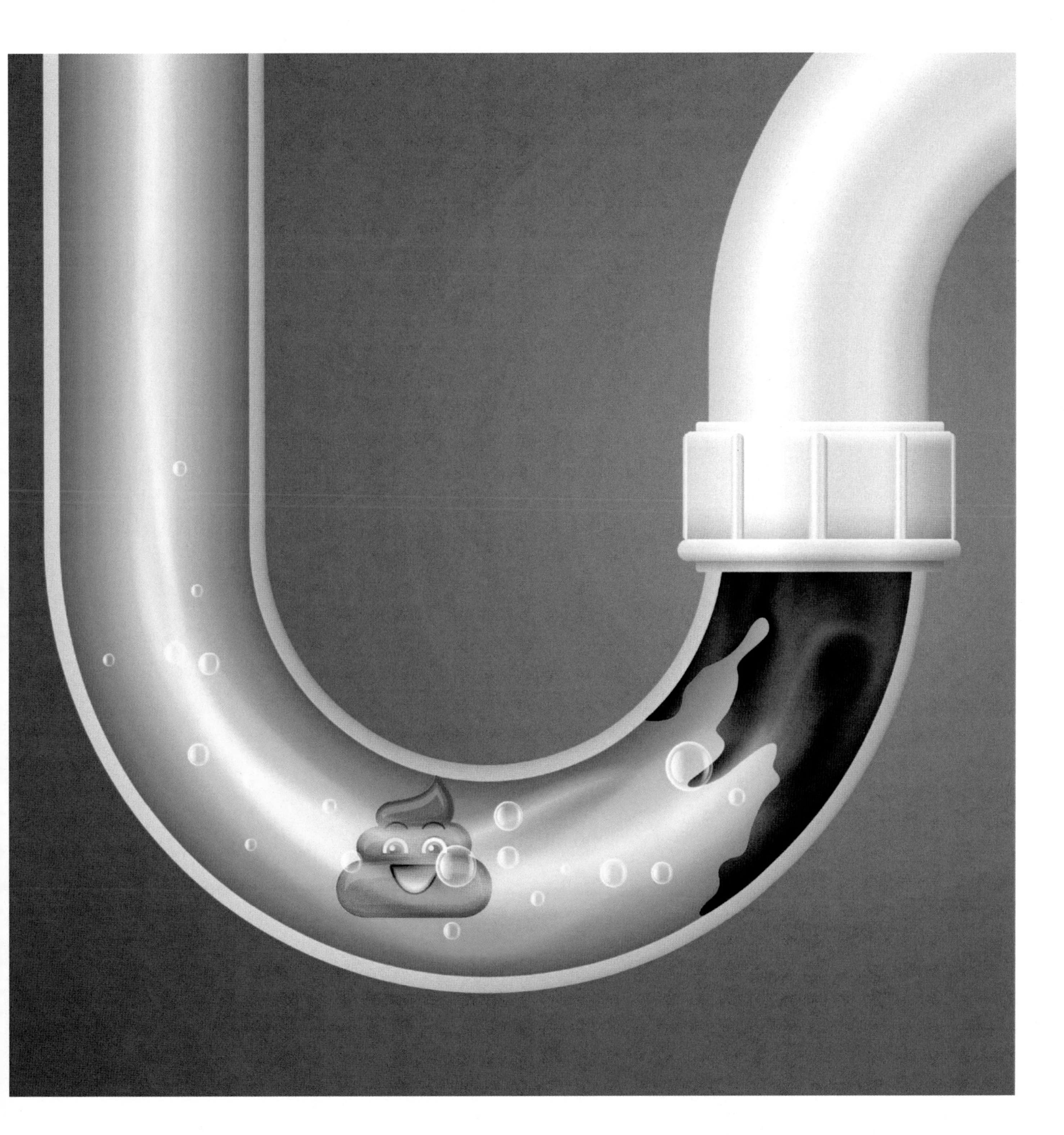

Big Turd finally squeezed through the hole.

Then my heart
swelled up with glee.

As Big Turd found Little Turd out in the sea.

Made in the USA
Monee, IL
05 May 2023